This

BBC toybox

Annual 2001

belongs to

Jonathan   Jonathan

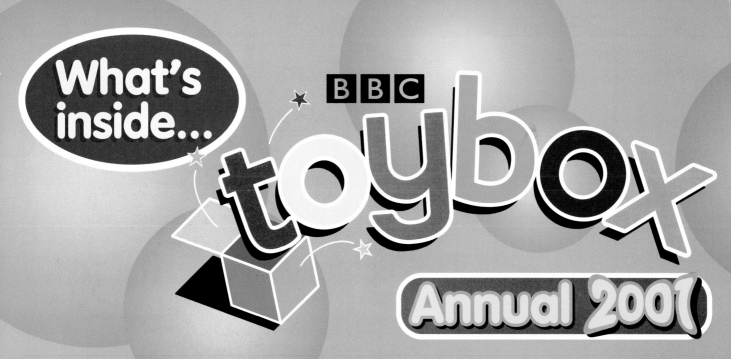

What's inside...

 2

I found this picture on page

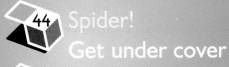

Tweenies
Dotman saves the day!

"The runaway train came down the track and she blew WOO! WOO!" sang Jake, Fizz, Milo and Bella as they ran behind each other, like train carriages, around the playroom. "Hang on, it's getting faster," squealed Milo. "It's running away with us," called Bella. "I can't slow down," shrieked Fizz, as they all ran faster. "We're going to go off the rails," screamed Bella.

"Don't worry, I'll save you. Dotman will save the train," said Jake, holding his hands up, pretending to stop the runaway train. It worked, everyone stopped.

"Jake what are you doing?" asked Bella.
"Hey, I'm Dotman. I'm being a superhero. WHEEE! YEAH! GAZZOOM! Today I saved the runaway train."

"Where did that thing come from?" asked Bella, pointing to Jake's colourful cape that was tucked neatly into his jumper.

"My mum made it - I'm Dotman da-nah!" announced Jake, proudly, raising his hand in the air as if he was about to fly away. "It's his superhero cape," explained Milo.

"It is. I'm going to be a superhero when I grow up. All superheroes wear these, don't they Milo?"

"Yes they dot - I mean do," giggled Milo.

"But why has it got coloured dots all over it?" asked Bella.

"Good question, Bella. Dotman looks after everybody's favourite colours. It is his job to save them if they disappear."

"I wouldn't like all the colours to disappear," said Bella, sadly.

Jake went over to look out the window. "Isn't the garden beautiful. All these lovely colours," he smiled.

Suddenly, the strangest thing happened. All the bright colours vanished from the garden. "Oh no! The colours have gone. Grey grass, grey trees, grey everything," said Jake, shocked. "This is a job for Dotman," continued Jake.

Dotman wasn't very pleased with the situation. "Oh no! The colours have gone. Where's the green of the grass, the blue of the sky, the yellow of the wall. It's all right garden, Dotman is here. It's *my* job to save the colours of the world. Dotman to the rescue," he announced bravely, as he leapt into action.

"Lots of lovely colours, nowhere to be seen, first I'll change the grass - grass, be green!" he sang.

With a flash, all the green re-appeared in the grass. But Dotman still had lots more work to do. He noticed even the wall and flowers had lost their beautiful colours. He decided to take care of the wall first. His cape blew in the wind as he sang some more superhero rhymes.

"Lots of lovely colours, Where are you? Hello! Wall be yellow!"

"WHEEEE!" he said happily, jumping in the air, thinking about his next task...

"Oh dear! Grey flowers, that can't be right - Dotman to the rescue, da-nah!" he said, before he zoomed in closer to them and used his superhero powers.

"Lots of lovely flowers and quicker than a wink, I'll save these weary flowers - flowers be pink!" he said. Suddenly all the bright colours re-appeared.

"Now, to restore the colours of the climbing frame in the garden."

He concentrated on his job, Then sang another superhero tune while whizzing down the slide.

"Lots of lovely colours. Come back here I said. Now I'll fix the climbing frame, be blue, purple, green and red."

Just then all the colours of the climbing frame were magically restored.

Dotman smiled. He was extremely happy with all of his hard work.

5

He folded his arms and laughed, "Dotman, that's me, the mighty. Think nothing of it. All in a days work."

Then Doodles came out into the garden to see what was going on. Just as Dotman was about to greet him, Doodles changed colour!

"Doodles, you're grey," he gasped. "Don't worry! Dotman will save you. I'll restore your colours!"

He quickly set to work. "Dotman's in charge of the colours. Doodles be red and yellow!" he commanded. Doodles barked happily as his colours returned.

"It's been a very colourful day today," said Dotman, looking around the garden.

"WOOF, WOOF!" agreed Doodles. It most certainly had. Thanks to Dotman.

Colouring-in

In the story, Dotman restored all the colours to the garden. You can be one of Dotman's helpers and colour in this fun picture of the Tweenies.

FIREMAN SAM
Sam's Sums

Help Fireman Sam with these sums. Write the answers in the boxes.

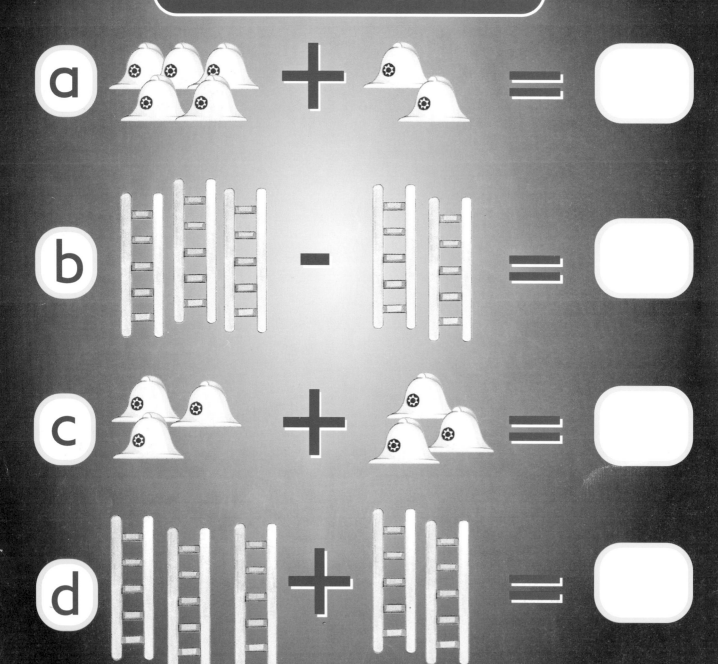

a) [ ] + [ ] = [ ]

b) [ ] - [ ] = [ ]

c) [ ] + [ ] = [ ]

d) [ ] + [ ] = [ ]

How many ladders are on this page? [ ]

How many helmets are on this page? [ ]

8

Tell the tale

9

Draw a line from each Teletubby to their favourite thing. Then have fun joining the dots and colouring the picture.

Teletubbies

Dot-to-dot

Party time!

Baz is having a birthday party for the ponies on Star Hill Farm. Look carefully at this fun picture, then answer the questions.

Star Hill Ponies

How many balloons can you see?

How many hats can you see?

How many ponies are celebrating ?

How many candles will be on your next birthday cake?

Now draw your birthday cake and candles in this box.

Buffalo Bob!

Bob was busy hammering some planks together. Scoop, Travis, Muck and Lofty were carrying more planks and lots of bales of hay into a field.

"I don't get it," said Muck. "There's a wooden floor, lights and all sorts of weird stuff in the field. What's happening here?"

"It's for the big line dancing contest tonight," said Scoop.

"What's that?" asked Lofty.

"It's American dancing like the cowboys do! You wear cowboy clothes and dance in a line," said Bob. "Grab your partner by the hand, step to the left and swing around!" he sang.

Bob started showing them how to line dance, but he forgot how the steps went and he looked very funny!

"Wow, Bob! You're, er, pretty good!" giggled Muck.

"Thanks, Muck," said Bob, proudly. "I'm entering the contest with Mavis from the post office. We've been going to classes for weeks." Lofty, Muck, Travis and

Scoop just looked at each other and laughed loudly.

At the office, Wendy let out a big sigh. "Life's just not fair is it?" she said to Pilchard. "I mean, *some* people will be dancing the night away tonight, and other people will just be going home and watching the telly – again!"

"Miaoow!" said Pilchard, nodding.

"I suppose I shouldn't grumble. Mavis and Bob have worked really hard. They deserve to win," said Wendy kindly.

Back at the yard, Bob was testing the microphone.

"Good. That's all working," he said, looking at his watch. "Oh no! Look at the time. I've got to get home for a bit of last-minute practice."

When Bob got home, he put on some music to practise his line dancing. Roley and Dizzy were in front of the house and heard the noise blasting out.

"Wow! That's the music they're going to dance to!" said Roley

14

excitedly.

"I like it. It makes me want to move about! Yee hah!" yelled Dizzy.

She raised herself up on two wheels and started to leap in the air like a bucking bronco. Pilchard held on tight to her mixer!

As the music came to an end, Bob was thinking about the contest.

"And the winners are Bob and Mavis!" he said.

Just then, Wendy poked her head around the door, but Bob was too busy bowing to his imaginary audience to notice!

"Bob!" she called. "It's Mavis on the phone."

Bob jumped and took the phone from her. When he got off the phone, he looked very upset.

"Mavis has sprained her ankle. There's no way she can dance tonight," Bob told Wendy.

"Oh, Bob. What a shame!" said Wendy with a sigh.

"I suppose I'll just have to cancel our entry," said Bob, sadly.

"Oh no! Don't do anything hasty, Bob!" said Wendy. "I mean, um, perhaps you could find another partner," she said, shyly.

"But I don't know anyone else, Wendy!" said Bob.

"Well, um, there's always me!" said Wendy. "I'm a fast learner and I'd love to give it a try!" said Wendy excitedly.

So Bob and Wendy set to work. Bob muddled up his steps and

Wendy shook her head. She showed him how to do it properly. In the end, their line dancing was perfect.

"Yee hah, Wendy! You're a fast learner all right!" said Bob, not realising that it was Wendy who had taught him!

That evening, Bob and Wendy got all dressed up in their line dancing clothes.

"You look funny!" giggled Dizzy, when she saw them. Then Scoop, Muck and Lofty arrived.

"Hey, Wendy, you look great. Where are you going?" asked Muck.

15

"Mavis has hurt her ankle, so I'm taking her place in the line dancing contest tonight," explained Wendy.

"We'd better get going or we'll be late. Wish us luck!" said Bob.

"Can they win it?" asked Scoop. "Yes they can!" laughed all the machines.

"Bye! I wish *we* could join in the contest," said Dizzy, still with Pilchard on her back.

Then Scoop had an idea. Pilchard went into the house and turned on the radio cassette with her paw. She started to nod her head to the music, happily, while Scoop, Muck and Lofty showed Roley and Dizzy how to do line dancing!

Later, at the contest, it was Bob and Wendy's turn. They were both feeling very nervous. But, as soon as they got on the dance floor, they did a fantastic dance. As the music came

to an end, the audience clapped very loudly.

"Thank you, Buffalo Bob and Western Wendy!" said the man on the microphone.

Bob took Wendy's hand and led her from the dance floor, happily.

The machines were wondering if Bob and Wendy had won the contest. They were so excited, they couldn't sleep.

"Thanks for a great evening, Bob," said Wendy, when Bob dropped her off at her house.

"You surely were a great partner!" laughed Bob, in an American accent.

As he walked home through the yard, Bob heard a noise.

"Psst, Bob!" whispered Muck. "Muck? Shhh. Everyone's asleep!" said Bob.

"Hee hee. I'm not," said Dizzy. "Tell us about the contest, Bob."

"Well, er, everyone, I'm afraid we won!" said Bob, showing them his trophy, proudly.

"Three cheers for Bob and Wendy," cheered the machines. "Hip, hip, hooray! Hip, hip, hooray! Hip, hip, hooray!"

Wendy heard the noise and peered out of her window. "Yee hah!" she cried, throwing her cowboy hat in the air triumphantly!

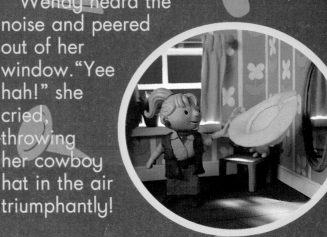

Copy and colour

Look carefully at the picture of Bob and Pilchard in the red grids. Then use a pencil to copy the drawing in the blue grids. When you've finished drawing you can colour them in. Can you do it? Yes you can!

What's changed?

Look carefully at these two pictures of Noddy's party
and circle the four differences on the bottom picture.

A

B

Next, please!

Work out who comes next in each line and draw them in the boxes.

19

Make a spider

You will need: •thin card •wool •safe scissors •coloured pipe cleaners •safe glue •beady eyes

Cut out two circles of thin card the same size, ask a grown-up to cut out holes in each. (Not smaller than 3 cm wide).

Keep both rings of card together while you wind the wool through the holes. Cover the rings with a few layers of wool.

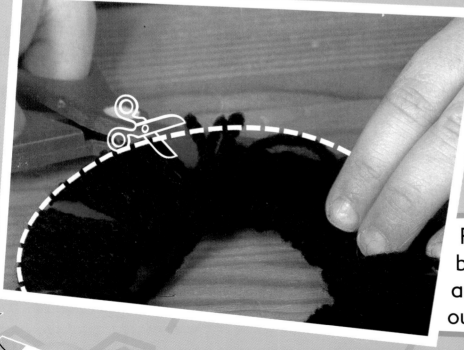

Push some scissors between both circles and cut around the outside edge.

Tie some wool between the two rings and knot it tightly. Pull the circles away.

Next, push four pipe cleaners through the ball to make the legs. Then, stick on some eyes.

Why not make a friend for your spider using different coloured wool?

ANGELMOUSE

Weather angels

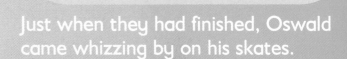

One day I went to my friend Angelmouse's house for breakfast. "I've run out of honey, Quilly," he said when he answered the door. He had tipped his honey pot upside down!

I quickly checked the cupboard for more honey. But all that was there was a letter from You-Know-Who for Angelmouse.

"Never mind that letter!" said Angelmouse. "I'm only a little angel and I have to do such a big lot of helping! I want my breakfast!" he grumbled, loudly.

I told him that's why his thingamajig was so shiny and he'd lose it if he stopped helping people. I read the note to him. It said "Little Petal needs your help."

"Oh, all right, let's go," said Angelmouse and off we went to Little Petal's shop. When we got there it was very messy. Angelmouse and Spencer offered to help her clean it.

Just when they had finished, Oswald came whizzing by on his skates.

"No brakes! No brakes!" he cried, before sending everyone spinning in a cloud of dust. The shop was now dirtier than it was before. Angelmouse decided it was too much of a tricky job and had an idea.

"Quick, Quilly, follow me. Let's go and see the weather angels. They're very important angels who will help."

We arrived in Seventh Heaven and knocked gently at the palace door. The Sun-Angel, Wind-Angel and Rain-Angel answered.

"Hello," they said looking around, but didn't seem to see us.

"There's no-one there," said the Rain-Angel.

"Yes there is. It's me, Angelmouse."

The three angels looked down at us.

"Do you know who we are?" asked the Sun-Angel.

"Yes, you're the Sun-Angel, the Wind-Angel and the Rain-Angel. I learned all about you in Angel school," replied Angelmouse.

"I hope you also learned that we are very important angels with lots of

"We've decided you're right," said the Sun-Angel. "You're only a small angel, but your work is just as important as ours. We all have to help each other. Now what would you like us to do for you?"

First of all, Angelmouse asked the Wind-Angel to blow away all the dust and dirt. Then Angelmouse asked the Rain-Angel to wash Little Petal's shop. Finally, he asked the Sun-Angel to dry the shop and make it sparkle with extra sunshine.

work to do. I hope you are not wasting our precious time."

"We're not. The thing is, Little Petal's shop needs to be cleaned today," said Angelmouse. The Rain-Angel looked slightly annoyed.

"That's better. Thank you so much for helping us, weather angels," said Angelmouse when they had finished.

"It's been a pleasure," they said, as they flew off.

Then Little Petal came out of her shop to take a look.

"Do you think that's important?" he asked.

"Well it is to her," replied Angelmouse. "She's very upset about it."

"Oh, Angelmouse! It's lovely! Did you do all of this?"

"I had a bit of help from the weather angels!" replied Angelmouse.

All of the weather angels looked strangely at Angelmouse and me.

Angelmouse continued. "When I was in Angel school, they said that if there was something that you couldn't do, you should always ask someone for help."

"You're my favourite angel, Angelmouse," smiled Little Petal.

"I see," said the Sun-Angel. He turned to the other angels and started whispering.

"They don't look very happy," said Angelmouse nervously.

Jungle journey

Find out how amazing the jungle can be by playing this exciting board game. Take turns with your friends to roll a dice and move around the board. First one to swing in the trees with the orang-utan is the winner!

Start

1

2

3

4

You meet a friendly elephant. Climb onto his tail and walk across him to number 7.

5

6

7

8

Uh-oh! This lion doesn't seem very happy. Roar back at him and then move on 2 spaces.

9

10

25

FIREMAN SAM™

It was Fireman Sam's day off, so James and Sarah went to visit him at home. "Uncle Sam!" they called, knocking at his door. "We've come to see you!" They waited a while, but there was no reply. "I know where he'll be," said James. "He'll be in his inventing shed!"

They found Sam hard at work. "What are you doing?" asked Sarah. "I'm making popcorn for us to take to the cinema," said Sam.

James and Sarah stared at a very strange machine. "This is my popcorn machine," said Sam. "Go and play outside until it's ready."

But as the children were playing, they heard a strange noise from the shed. "Help!" cried Sam. "My machine's going to explode!"

"We'll help!" cried James and Sarah and they called the fire station. Elvis and Station Officer Steele came to the rescue…

…but they were too late! The inventing shed exploded with a very loud BANG! "Are you OK, Uncle Sam?" yelled James.

"I'm fine," said Sam, walking out with a bowl of burnt popcorn. "But I think we'll have to buy our popcorn at the cinema tonight!"

Wishful thinking

Read the poem and circle the picture of the correct wish in each verse.

If I could wish upon a star,
I'd wish for a bright, pink guitar.
I'd play it morning, noon and night,
Much to everyone's delight!

If I could wish on another star,
I'd wish for a fast, red, shiny car.
I'd drive it on my way to school,
And all my friends would think I'm cool.

If I could have another wish,
I'd ask for a very tasty dish
Of all the favourite foods I like,
Or maybe I'd wish for a new bike?

And if I could have one more thing,
I'd ask for a magic wishing ring.
Then if there's something I forgot,
I could ask until I had the lot!

This wishing thing is very tricky,
Or maybe I'm a bit too picky.
You can choose from all this stuff,
After all I have enough.

Scary Stories

One night, Peggy, Poppy and Why were telling each other scary stories. "That was really creepy!" shivered Peggy.

"Yes it was," agreed Why, peering out from behind her pillow. "Can we sleep with the lights on?"

"I wasn't scared," said Poppy, bravely. "It was only a story. Monsters don't really exist."

Poppy turned out the lights and went to bed. "Poppy is right, but she isn't that brave," said Peggy.

Peggy and Why decided to play a trick on Poppy. They tiptoed quietly out of the room...

"Let's pretend to be ghosts that will definitely scare her!" said Why. So they dressed up in big sheets.

"OOOOOOH!" wailed Peggy and Why, as they stood in the doorway, waggling their arms.

Poppy sat up in bed and shrieked. "G-g-g-g-ghosts!" she cried and leapt quickly out of bed.

Peggy and Why chased Poppy round and round the bedroom. "WOOOOH!" they moaned.

Suddenly Peggy and Why started to giggle. "Fooled you, Poppy!" they said. Poppy felt very silly.

Perhaps I'm not so brave," said Poppy. "No," giggled Why. "You're just a big scaredy-cat!"

At school, William's teacher was teaching his class all about the dinosaurs. "I'd love to have a dinosaur as a pet," said William excitedly.

William's teacher shook his head. "That's impossible, William," he said. "All dinosaurs died out a very long time ago!"

But when lunch time came, William was still thinking about dinosaurs. "I think a pet dinosaur would be fun!" he thought.

So, William wished very hard and suddenly a huge foot slammed down next to him, making him jump.

The foot belonged to a huge Tyrannosaurus Rex who looked very fierce.

"Ooh, er, hello!" gasped William. "You're very big."

"And I'm extremely hungry!" growled the dinosaur, rudely.

William reached inside his school bag and took out a ham sandwich. "You can have my lunch if you like," he said.

The dinosaur bent down and took the sandwich with his big, wet tongue. "I want more, more, MORE!" it roared.

The dinosaur looked round and saw William's friends nearby, eating their lunch. He licked his lips and ate all their food!

William's friends began to cry. "Stop, stop!" shouted William. "You're just too rude and greedy. I wish I had a dinosaur that didn't eat meat."

Suddenly, the greedy Tyrannosaurus Rex changed into a long-necked Diplodocus.

"That's better," said William, as the dinosaur happily started munching the leaves off a tree.

But the Diplodocus didn't just like trees. It saw a garden hedge that had been cut into different animal shapes. The dinosaur went up to it and took a big bite out of a duck!

"Stop it, you dippy Diplodocus!" cried William. "You'll get us all into really big trouble."

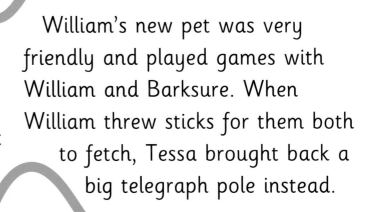

William took the Dinosaur away, but it got stuck as it tried to go under a bridge. William decided he needed to get a different dinosaur.

"I'm sorry, Dippy," he sighed. "I think I need a smaller, friendly dinosaur for a pet."

William wished again and he got a baby Triceratops called Tessa. She licked William's face with her tongue. "Ooh, stop it!" William giggled. "That's so tickly!"

William's new pet was very friendly and played games with William and Barksure. When William threw sticks for them both to fetch, Tessa brought back a big telegraph pole instead.

She used her big horn to dig holes in the garden, so Barksure could bury his bones!

She even gave William rides on her back. "Hey, this is great fun, isn't it?" cried William.

"Well, yes and no," sighed Tessa. "I like playing with you, but I really miss my dinosaur friends back home, a lot."

"Oh, I see," said William, frowning. "I suppose I'd better wish you back home, then!"

"Yes, I suppose so," nodded Tessa. William felt sad as she disappeared. "But never mind, though," he said to Barksure. "At least I've still got you and my wish wellingtons!"

How much of the story do you remember? Roar like a dinosaur when you get a question right!

What did William give the Tyrannosaurus Rex to eat?

Why were William's friends upset with the Tyrannosaurus Rex?

Why did Tessa want to go back home?

Would **you** like to have a pet dinosaur?

35

William's colouring-in

Can you tell what William is sitting on? Join the dots to find out.

If you had a pet dinosaur, what would you call it? Write the name in this box.

Chit chat!

Write what you think Baz is saying to Thomas in the speech bubble. Then answer the questions about the picture below.

- Where do you think Baz and Thomas are going?
- Which would you prefer to ride - a bike or a pony?
- Now make up a story about the picture.

37

Sing and dance

Sing with Laa-Laa, touch your toes,
Jump like Po, how high she goes!

Dance like Dipsy, bend your knee,
Stretch and march – like Tinky Winky!

Teletubbies

Bouncing, jumping in and out,
Up and down and round about!

Colourful cakes!

To make these delicious cakes, you will need: ● 100g of self-raising flour ● 100g of soft margarine ● 100g of caster sugar ● 2 eggs
For the icing you will need: ●100g of icing sugar ● food colouring ● 100g of soft butter ● sweets or other cake decorations

Sieve the flour into a bowl. Add the margarine and caster sugar and mix it all together, just like Poppy is doing!

Carefully break the eggs into the bowl. Beat everything together with a wooden spoon until the mixture is soft and creamy.

Put your cake mixture into paper cake cases. You'll need to put two spoonfuls into each one.

Ask a grown-up to bake your cakes for 20 to 25 minutes at 180°C (350°F/gas mark 4). Then leave them on a wire rack to cool.

Now you're ready to ice and decorate your cakes!

Put the butter into a bowl and cut it up into small pieces. Beat it until it is creamy, then sift in the icing sugar, a little at a time.

Add some food colouring. Then carefully spread some icing on top of each cake. Add any decorations before the icing dries.

And finally it's time to eat your cakes with a nice drink!

Amazing gardens

Help Baz find the quickest route to get to the ponies. Have fun working your way through the maze to the carrot patch. Then answer Jim's questions at the end.

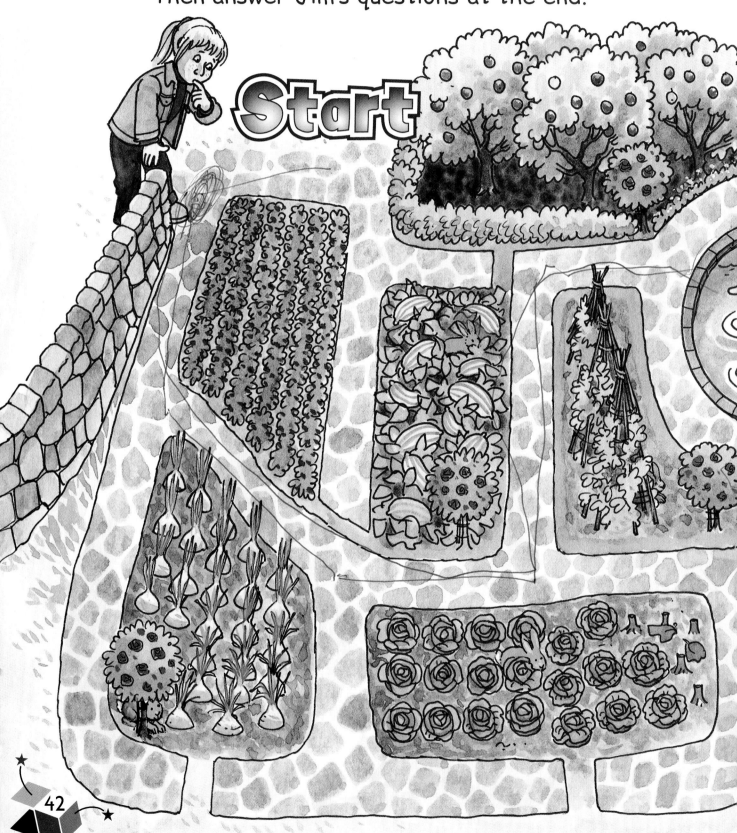

42

Star Hill Ponies

Finish

1) How many rose bushes are there in the picture?

2) How many ducks are swimming in the pond?

3) Do you know the names of the ponies in the picture?

4) Where are Jim's spade and wheelbarrow?

5) There are some rabbits hidden in the garden. How many can you find?

43

Answers: 1) 7 rose bushes. 2) 5 ducks. 3) Molly, Dylan and Scruffy. 4) They are near the fence. 5) 6 rabbits.

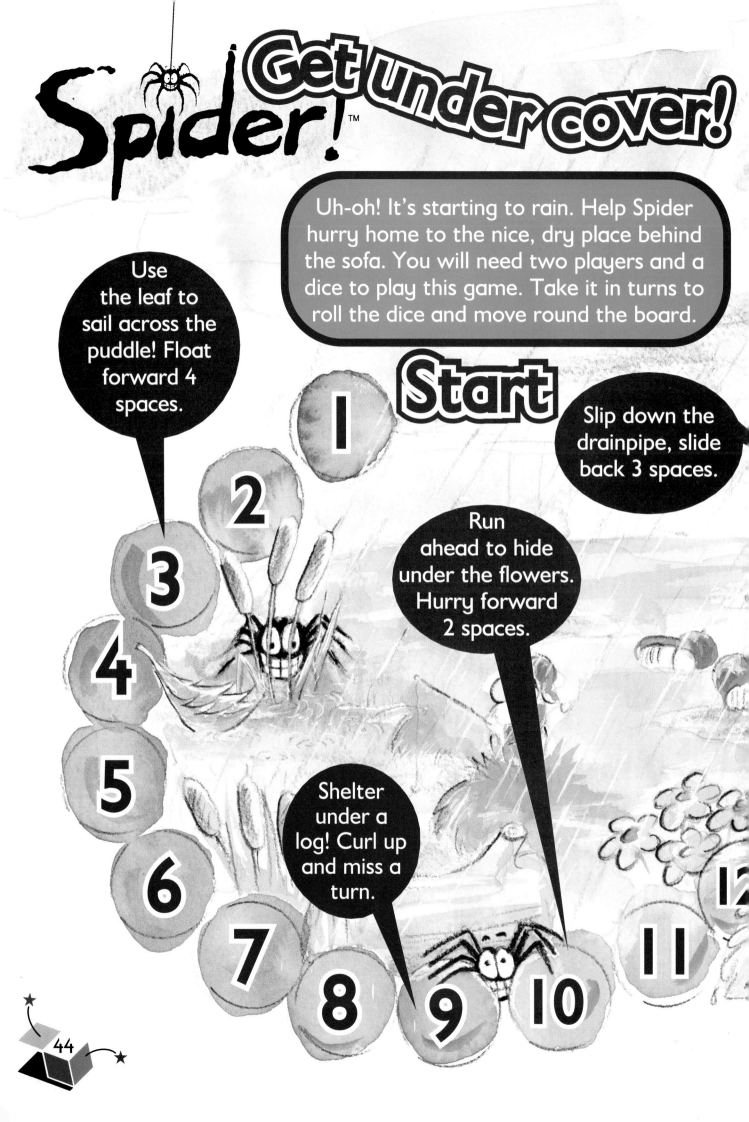

Cloud hopping!

By playing this colouring-in board game with your friends, you can find out how Angelmouse got his angel licence. You will need some crayons to colour in the blank parts of the game.

6

Start

1

5

4

2   3

12

Angelmouse was naughty at Angel school. Miss a go, while you colour in the cloud that he has to sit on.

13

14

15

Be careful! You've just bumped into Quilly. Miss a go to colour him in!

16

Good work for saving Quilly from flying into the windmill. Colour it in and take another go.

18

17

46

ANGELMOUSE

Help the angel to colour in this rainbow then move on 2 spaces.

7

8

9

10

11

Finish

20

19

Look at the panel to see what the message should say. Write it in the space and you've won!

Now make up a story about what happened to Angelmouse in this game.

Look at this list everytime you need to colour in something on the game. What order should they go in? Write the order in the boxes.

well done !

The dancing competition

One evening, Noddy and Big-Ears were in Noddy's garden when they heard a noise. They looked over the fence and saw Mr and Mrs Tubby Bear moving around strangely, holding hands.

"What are you doing?" asked Noddy, looking puzzled.

"We're practising for the Toy Town Dancing Competition," said Mrs Tubby Bear.

Soon, the day of the competition arrived. All the toys gathered in the market square.

Just then, Tessie Bear and Bumpy Dog came along.

"Noddy, will you be my partner in the dancing competition please?" asked Tessie Bear, excitedly.

"I'm sorry, but I can't dance," said Noddy.

"Don't worry, Noddy," said Big-Ears. "I'll teach you some great dance steps."

So the next day, Tessie and Noddy went to Toadstool House for a dancing lesson.

"Left, right, left, right," called Big-Ears, as Tessie and Noddy danced round the room.

"You're a good dancer, Noddy," said Big-Ears.

"It gives me great pleasure to announce that the Toy Town Dancing Competition will now begin," said Mr Plod. All the toys clapped and cheered excitedly.

Sly and Gobbo were watching nearby. "Why are we entering a dancing competition?" asked Sly.

"We're not, we're just going to ruin it for everyone else!" laughed Gobbo, as he sneaked over to the record player and opened it.

49

The two goblins took out some of the important parts.

Then they quickly ran off.

Mr Wobbly Man went over to the record player and turned it on, but there was no sound coming from it.

"Oh dear," said Mr Wobbly Man. "The record player doesn't seem to be working."

"Someone has stolen some of the parts," said Mr Plod, as he opened it up. "Now the competition can't take place."

But then Noddy had an idea.

"Big-Ears, do you have your old record player at home?" he asked.
"Yes, Noddy, I certainly do. What a great idea! You are clever, Noddy," said Big-Ears.

Noddy drove him home to collect it.

Soon, they returned with the record player and, at last, the competition began.

But then Sly and Gobbo tried to steal the prize trophy.

"What are you doing?" said Mr Plod, when he spotted them behaving oddly.

"Er, Mr Plod, we'd like to win this beautiful trophy!" said Gobbo, quickly.

"Well, if you want to win the trophy, you'll have to dance for it!" Mr Plod, replied sternly.

Sly and Gobbo looked at each other, frowning.

"Come on, Sly," said Gobbo, taking his hand.

So the two goblins started to dance. They did look very funny!

"Who are the winners of the competition?" asked Mr Plod, when everyone had finished dancing.

Mrs Noah, Mr Milko and Sally Skittle were the judges. They whispered among themselves.

"The prize for the most unusual dance, goes to the goblins, Sly and Gobbo!" announced Mrs Noah.

"But the overall winners of the silver trophy for the best dancers in the Toy Town Dancing Competition are Tessie and Noddy!

"Hooray!" cried everyone, as Mr Plod handed them the trophy.

Then, Mr Plod asked Noddy and Tessie to do their great dance again. Everyone cheered.

"I really do like dancing, Tessie," said Noddy happily. "Big-Ears is a really good teacher," he laughed.

"He certainly is," said Tessie, smiling as they started dancing again for the toys.

And they danced and danced and danced!

Each time you answer a question correctly, tick the box.

● How did Big-Ears help Noddy?

● What did Sly and Gobbo do to the record player?

● Who were the judges of the competition?

52

Colouring-in

53

Teletubbies Balloons

One day in Teletubbyland, something new appeared from far away – balloons! Follow each ribbon with your finger to match each Teletubby to their balloon. Whose balloon needs to be coloured in?

Spot the differences

Look carefully at these pictures and see if you can spot the differences in the bottom picture.

A

B

55

Make-it! Piggy bank

Remember it takes a day for each layer of papier-mâché to dry!

To make a papier-mâché piggy bank, to help Baz save for her pony fund, you will need: ◆ a balloon ◆ a cardboard tube ◆ newspaper ◆ flour and water ◆ paint ◆ thin card ◆ paintbrush ◆ safe scissors ◆ sticky tape ◆ beady eyes ◆ a pipe cleaner

Week 1

First, blow up a small balloon and cut the cardboard tube into four even pieces for the legs.

Mix two spoons of flour and two spoons of water together to make the paste.

Soak some newspaper strips in the paste and use them to cover the balloon. The more layers you do the stronger your piggy bank will be!

When it has dried out, ask a grown-up to burst the balloon with a pin. Then stick on the legs, and paint your piggy bank. Let the paint dry.

Cut out the ears and snout from thin card - don't forget to colour in the nostrils! Then stick on some beady eyes.

Twist a pink pipe cleaner into the shape of a curly tail and stick it onto the back of the piggy bank.

Ask a grown-up to cut a slot in the top of your piggy bank - then it's finished!

Are you ready to sing?

It's Song Time! Join in the fun with the Tweenies by singing and doing the actions to this song.

Five little ducks went swimming one day,
Over the hills and far away.
Mother Duck said, "Quack, quack, quack, quack."
But only four little ducks came back.

> Five little ducks went swimming one day,

> Over the hills and far away.

Hold your arms out in front, then pull them apart as if you were swimming.

Four little ducks went swimming one day,
Over the hills and far away.
Mother Duck said, "Quack, quack, quack, quack."
But only three little ducks came back.

Stand on one leg and point to the hills far away.

58

Tweenies™

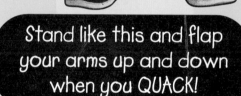

Mother Duck said, "Quack, quack, quack, quack."

Three little ducks went swimming one day,
Over the hills and far away.
Mother Duck said, "Quack, quack, quack, quack."
But only two little ducks came back.

But only one little duck came back.

Stand like this and flap your arms up and down when you QUACK!

Two little ducks went swimming one day,
Over the hills and far away.
Mother Duck said, "Quack, quack, quack, quack."
But only one little duck came back.

Hold your head and look puzzled when you sing about the ducks that came back.

One little duck went swimming one day,
Over the hills and far away.
Mother Duck said, "Quack, quack, quack, quack."
And all five little ducks came back.

Busy Bob

Start

Find out just how busy Bob really is by playing this fun board game with your friends. All you have to do is roll a dice and take turns to move round the board.

8

1 The phone hasn't stopped ringing all morning. Move forward 2 spaces to your first job.

7

3 **2**

6

4

Mrs Potts' radiator is causing trouble. Miss a go while you fix it.

You do a great job with your crew mending the road. Take another go!

5